RELAXING
DOT-TO-DOT
ANIMAL KINGDOM

SEVENOAKS

Introduction

Are you ready for a new challenge? *Relaxing Dot-to-Dot: Animal Kingdom* is a collection that celebrates animals from around the world. Here are fierce predators—as well as their prey. Discover as well the many animals that are now facing extinction, endangered by the activity of humans.

To reveal each animal, you'll have to join together 1,001 numbered dots. That's sure to take time, and you will need to focus. These puzzles ask for commitment. Think of this as your opportunity: This is the moment you get to shut down the computer and turn off the television. With nothing to distract you, these puzzles will help you relax. What's more, they're sure to intrigue. Here is an animal that follows the rains; a bird that cools down by using its beak; a monkey that moves so carefully it makes no sound; and a scavenger that helps halt the spread of disease.

Revealing the images on some pages may sometimes be difficult, because the dots are massed together. Where they are, we've used darker colors for numbers to guide you. And if you do get stuck, all the solutions are printed at the back of the book.

As you reveal each picture, you'll learn about a bird so small it can be trapped in a spider web, and a bird that seals itself within its own nest. You'll learn about a mammal that lets algae grow in its fur, and a reptile whose scales refract the light. There are animals that use tools, a bird that understands words, and a pig that can survive for months without water.

Completing all the images in the book will mean joining together more than forty thousand dots. That's no chore; it's an achievement. So sharpen your pencils, and get ready to explore the extraordinary and diverse world of *Relaxing Dot-to-Dot: Animal Kingdom*.

1. Parrots

We know parrots best for their ability to speak, an ability that varies hugely between species. Some parrots are simply mimics, with a memory that can hold hundreds, even thousands of words. Others, however, seem to understand what is said and can respond. The African Grey talks at the level of a four- or five-year-old child, and may learn numbers, colors, and shapes.

2. Giraffe

A giraffe eats about 75 pounds (34 kilograms) per day, but double that has been recorded. Their effect on trees is beneficial, trimming trees that have grown too tall and delaying the growth of younger ones. Because it is males that stretch for the highest leaves, a giraffe's posture while eating offers easy identification. Incidentally, although this is the tallest living animal, the giraffe actually takes its name from the Arabic for "fast walker."

3. Gorilla

Gorillas are intelligent animals. Using up to 25 distinct sounds, they can communicate even in dense forest. They also use tools: a stick to measure the depth of a swamp, and rocks to smash open nuts. A female gorilla observed in the wild showed remarkable intelligence. After seeing a young male pull his hand out of a hole and run away, she picked up a twig to forage for ants without being bitten.

4. Spider Monkey

It's their long limbs and tail that gives spider monkeys their name. Found in the forests of Central and South America, they spend their lives in the treetops, and their powerful tail helps them move quickly through dense vegetation. While on lookout duty, monkeys stand on two feet, using the tail as support. The big toe on their feet is elongated, offering a better grip on thinner branches.

5. Elephant

Elephants are depicted on rock paintings from the Paleolithic Era, which began more than two million years ago. Today, elephants face extinction. The principal threat is poachers killing them for their tusks. Unfortunately, the longer tusks that are so prized are found on older, healthier elephants. Breeding from weaker animals could endanger the whole population. What's more, a male elephant starts to breed only when he reaches about 40 years old.

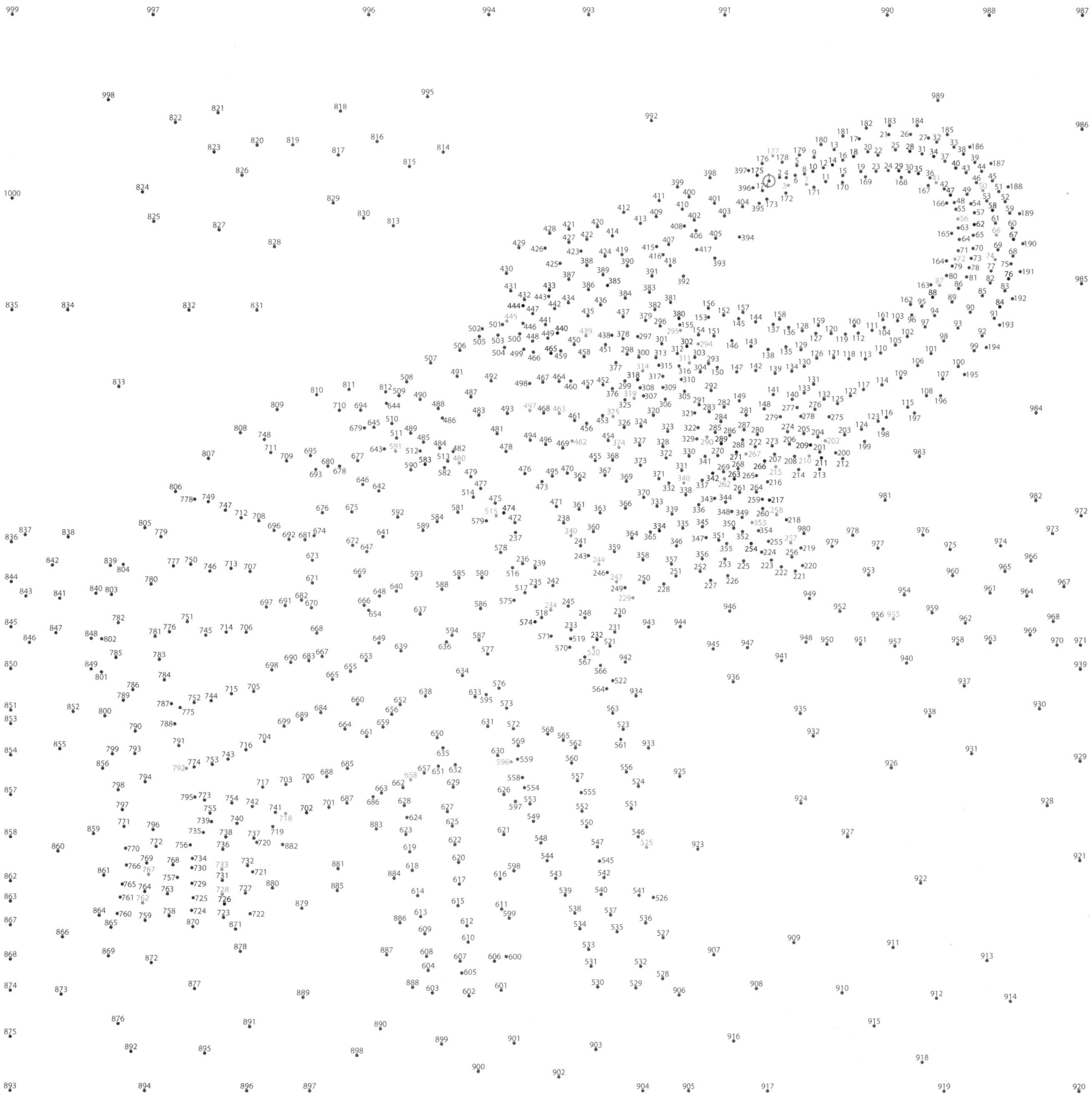

6. Chimpanzee

The chimpanzee is our closest living relative, so it is fitting that the name derives from a Bantu word meaning "mock man." These intelligent primates have been observed making plans for the future, appreciating the beauty of a sunset, and taking an interest in other wildlife that is neither threat nor prey. In captivity, chimps have been seen using mirrors, recognizing that, for example, their teeth need cleaning.

7. Panda

Pandas are the oldest bear, veering off from the rest of the family about seven million years ago. They once roamed across Asia, and it was probably human activity that drove them into the mountains of southwest China. There, they adapted to a diet of bamboo, which is so poor in nutrients that they cannot store enough fat reserves to hibernate. Another factor for their dwindling numbers is that females ovulate just once a year.

8. Red-Eye Frog

Its red eyes offer this green frog remarkable protection. Hiding among a tree's leaves during the day, it is well camouflaged. If threatened, it opens its eyes and jumps away. The red frightens predators by suggesting it is poisonous (it isn't), and it may also be confusing. Once landed in a new spot, the frog closes its eyes, the red disappears, and the green frog is camouflaged once again.

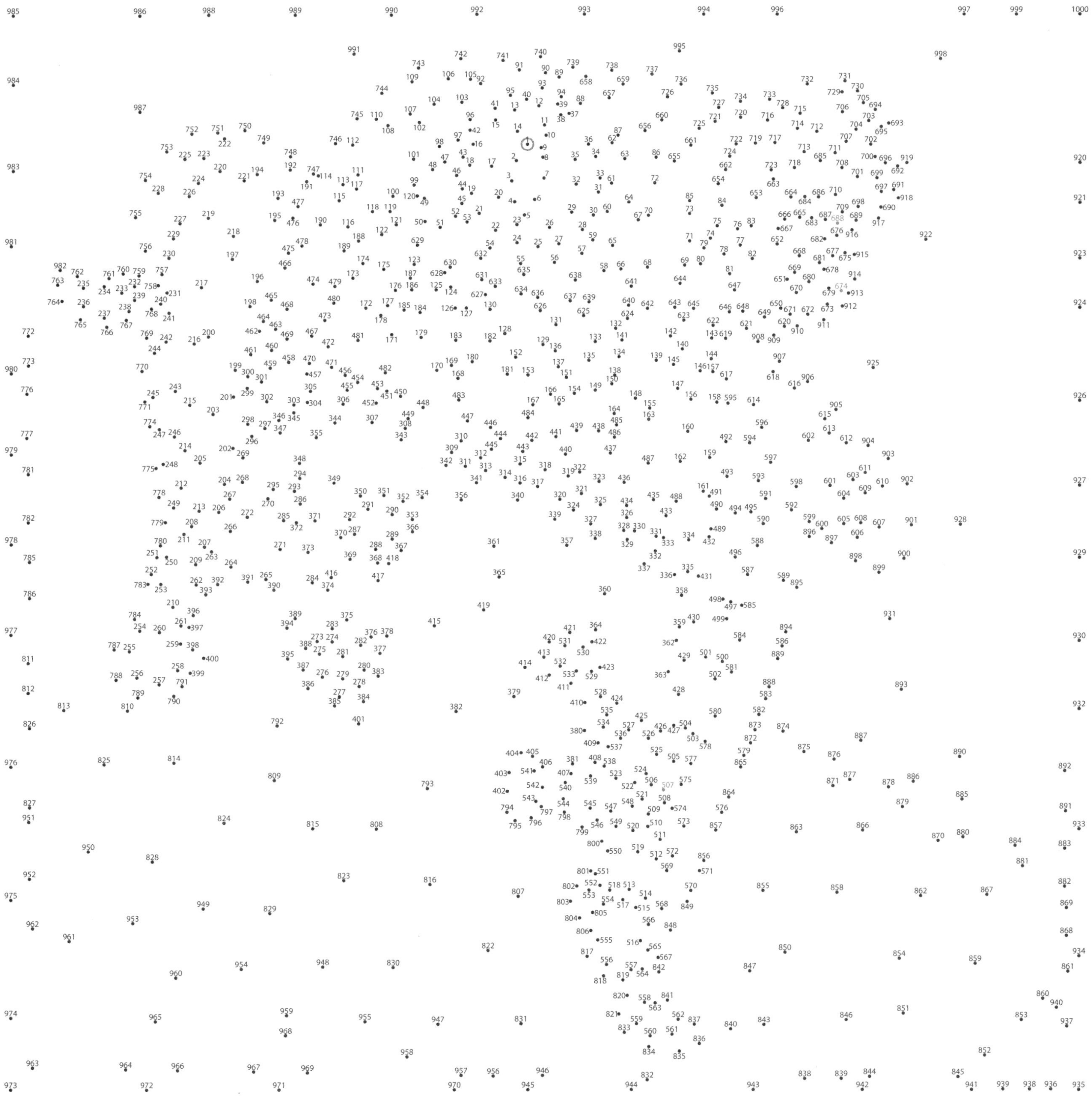

9. Lizard

A lizard relies on its tongue for its sense of smell. The tongue catches scent particles in the air, and sensory cells on the roof of the mouth then help the lizard to find food or a mate and to detect predators. Snakes, their closest living relatives, use their tongues in the same way. Like snakes, they do not have earflaps and catch sound via ear openings.

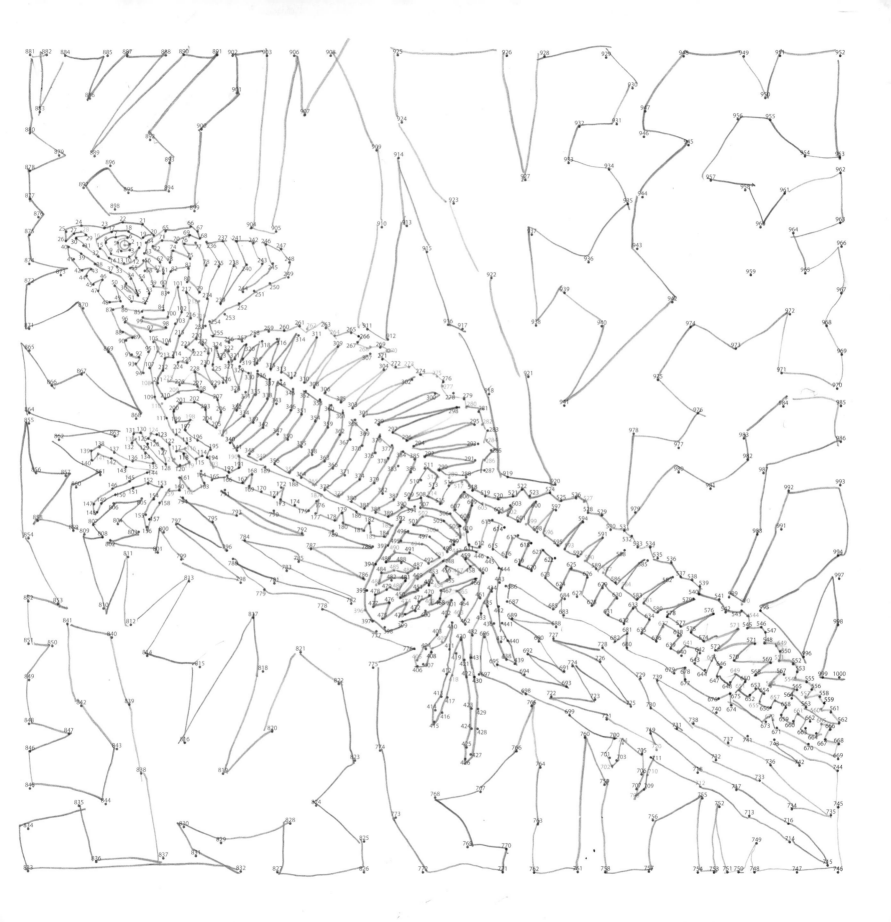

10. Spotted Hyena

The spotted hyena is also called the laughing hyena. However, their laughter is a sign of aggression. A pack of hyenas can be heard laughing over a kill, but each animal is fighting for access to meat. Any nips or scratches will evoke laughter in response. Incidentally, hyenas are not the scavengers they are assumed to be. They are efficient predators, with more than two-thirds of their diet being animals they have killed.

11. Chameleon

How do chameleons change color? It's a simple question, but recently the answer has changed. It was once assumed that the color changed as pigments were accumulated into or dispersed out of its cells. In fact, chameleons have two layers of iridophore cells that not only contain pigments but also reflect light. As the skin relaxes or contracts, light is reflected differently. Blue, for example, indicates a chameleon that is relaxed.

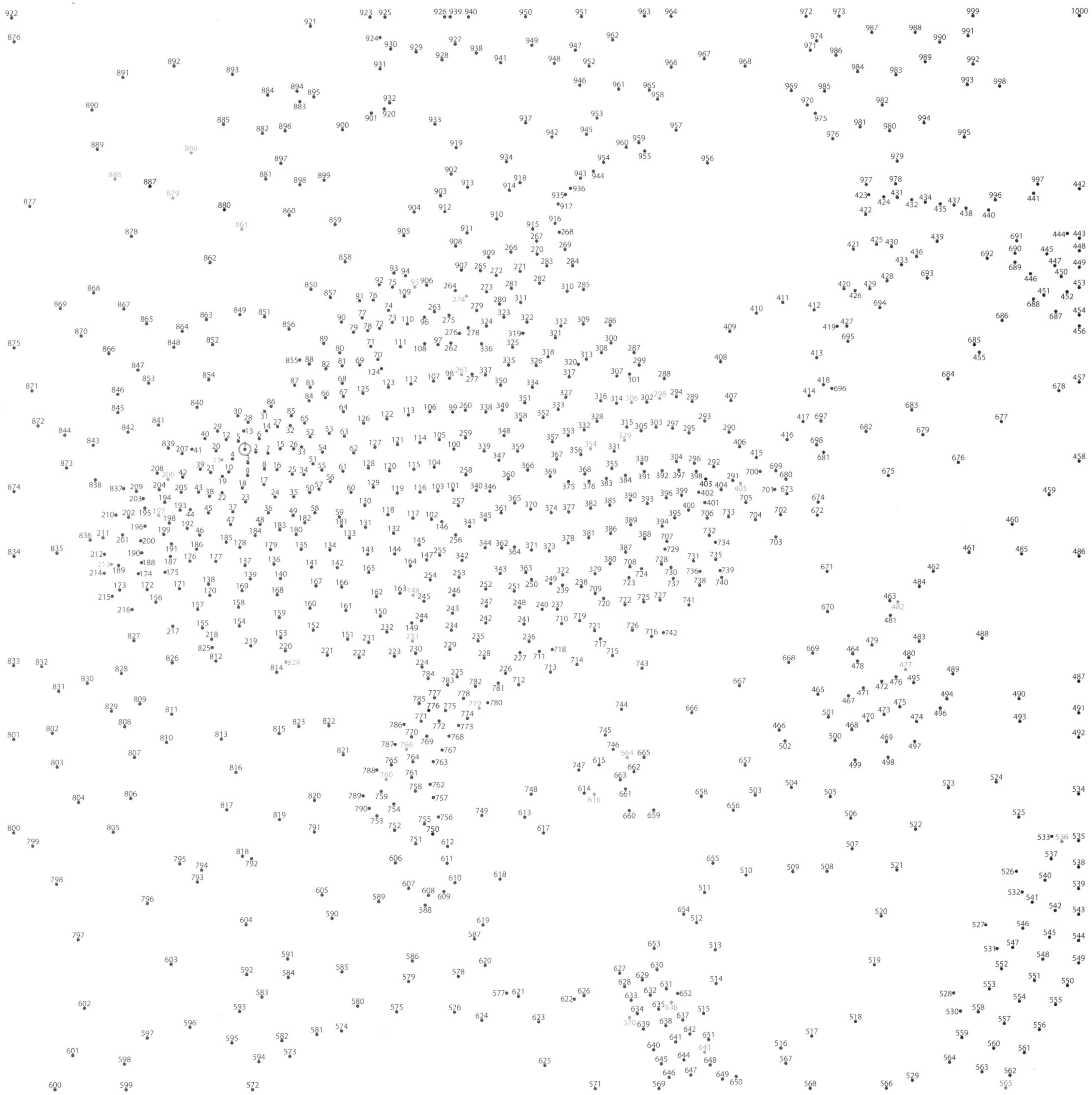

12. Zebra

Zebras are black animals with white stripes. (The opposite was once thought to be true.) The reason for those stripes is still debated. They may be a form of camouflage, but their main predators have poor vision and often hunt at night. They may be a form of identification; the pattern of the stripes is unique to each zebra. Or they may help cool the animal; air moves quickly over dark colors and slowly over light, so stripes create air currents.

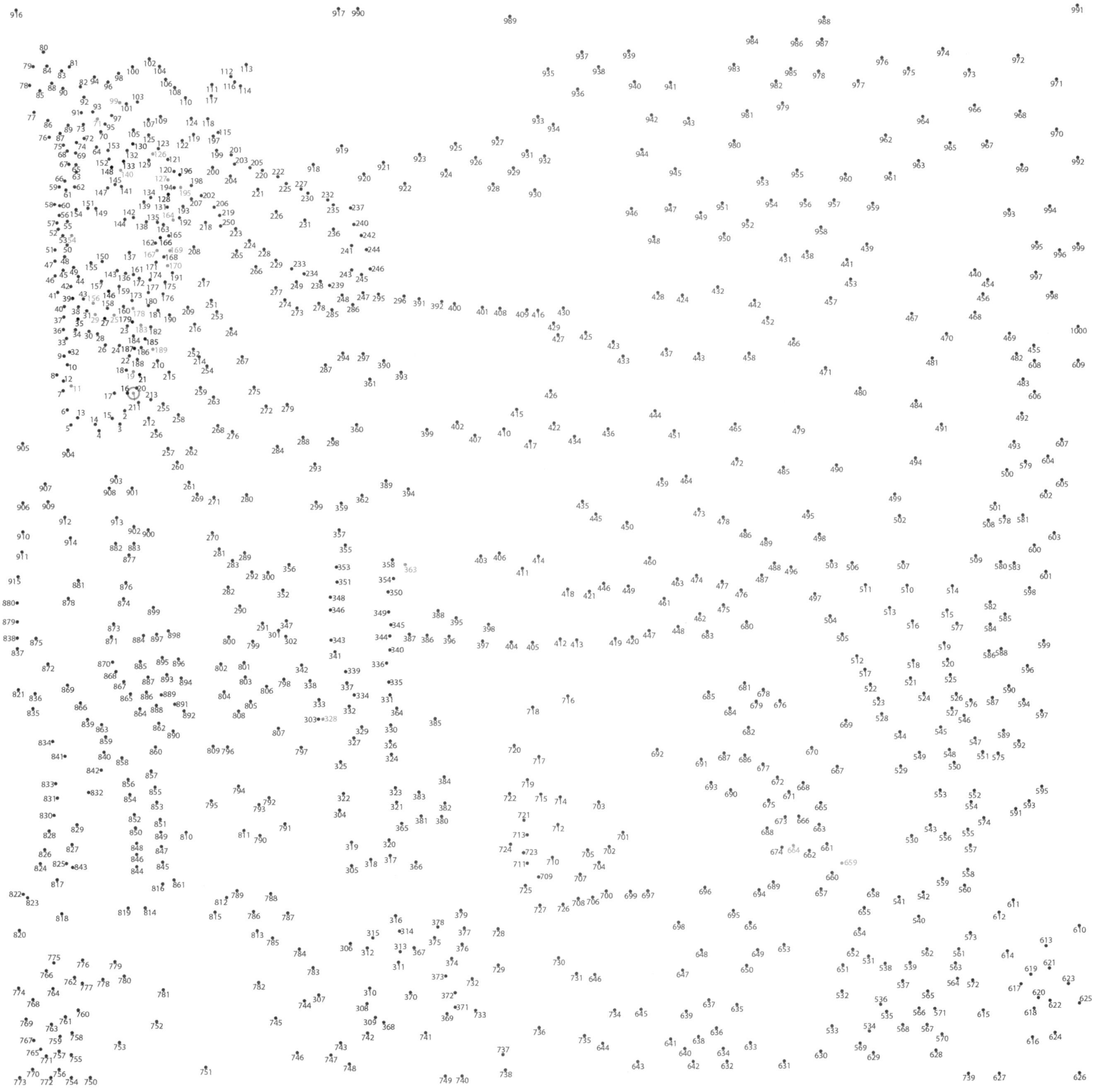

13. Rhinoceros

The horn of the rhinoceros has long been used in traditional medicines, and today the species is under threat. The black rhino has been declared extinct in West Africa. A subspecies of white rhino is probably extinct in Central Africa. The Javan rhino now exists only in Java, where there are about only 60 animals left. And the Sumatran rhino can no longer be found in Sumatra.

14. Lions

Lions generally hunt together. Attacking as a group minimizes the danger to individuals and enables the hunting of larger prey. Hunting usually takes place in darkness (avoiding moonlight) or in poor light (morning or evening), and the lions will spread out to cover a large area. It is common to see the younger lions driving their prey towards the older, more experienced members of the group.

15. Vulture

Vultures get bad press, but these birds play a vital role in maintaining the health of their environments. As scavengers, they rarely attack, and when they do, it is usually diseased or wounded animals that fall prey. Their stomach acid is so corrosive that vultures can feast on carcasses infected with botulism, rabies, classical swine fever, and even anthrax. This helps to minimize, even halt, the spread of disease.

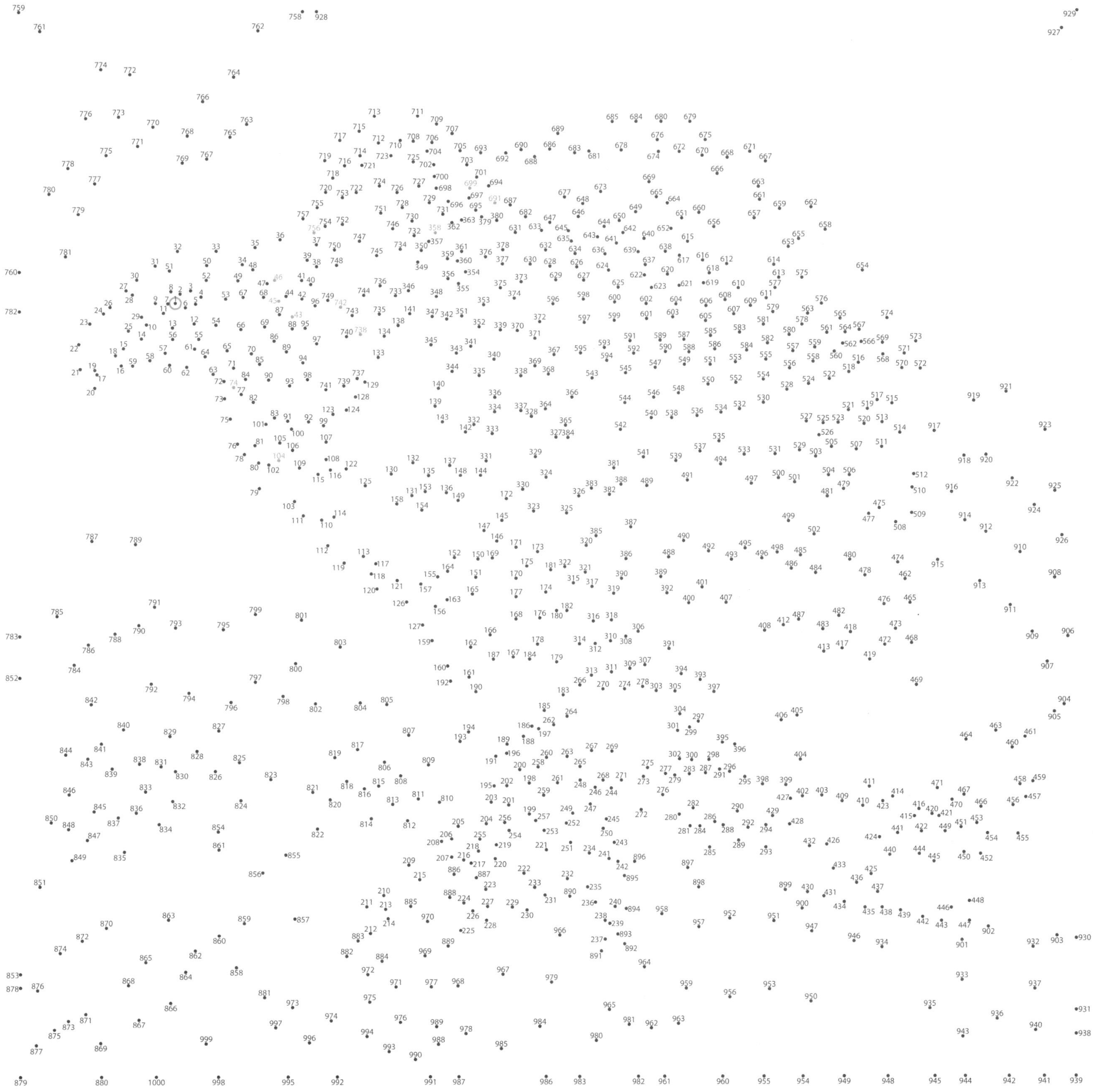

16. Hippopotamus

It's stocky, it's shaped like a barrel, and it's one of the most dangerous animals in Africa. Aggressive and unpredictable, the hippo will attack humans without apparent provocation. And although crocodiles successfully prey on younger hippos, adults often kill them or force them from their territory. Such behavior has earned this mammal quite a reputation. A Zulu warrior praised for his courage was not a "lionheart" but a "hippopotamus."

17. Slow Loris

They are slow, hence the name, but this lack of speed does offer advantages. These primates make barely any noise while moving through the forests where they live, and if they do attract attention, they immediately freeze. They have another defense: Lorises are the only primates to have a toxic bite. Licking glands near the elbow releases a toxin that is activated by saliva, and their bite will probably induce anaphylactic shock.

18. Gazelles

Gazelles may live in herds of ten or several hundred and are often found on plains. They are highly visible, and so highly vulnerable, to predators. Their defense is not their horns so much as their speed. For short distances, some species can sprint at 60 miles per hour (100 kilometers per hour), and they can sustain speeds of 30–40 miles an hour (50–64 kilometers per hour). This may enable them to outrun a lion.

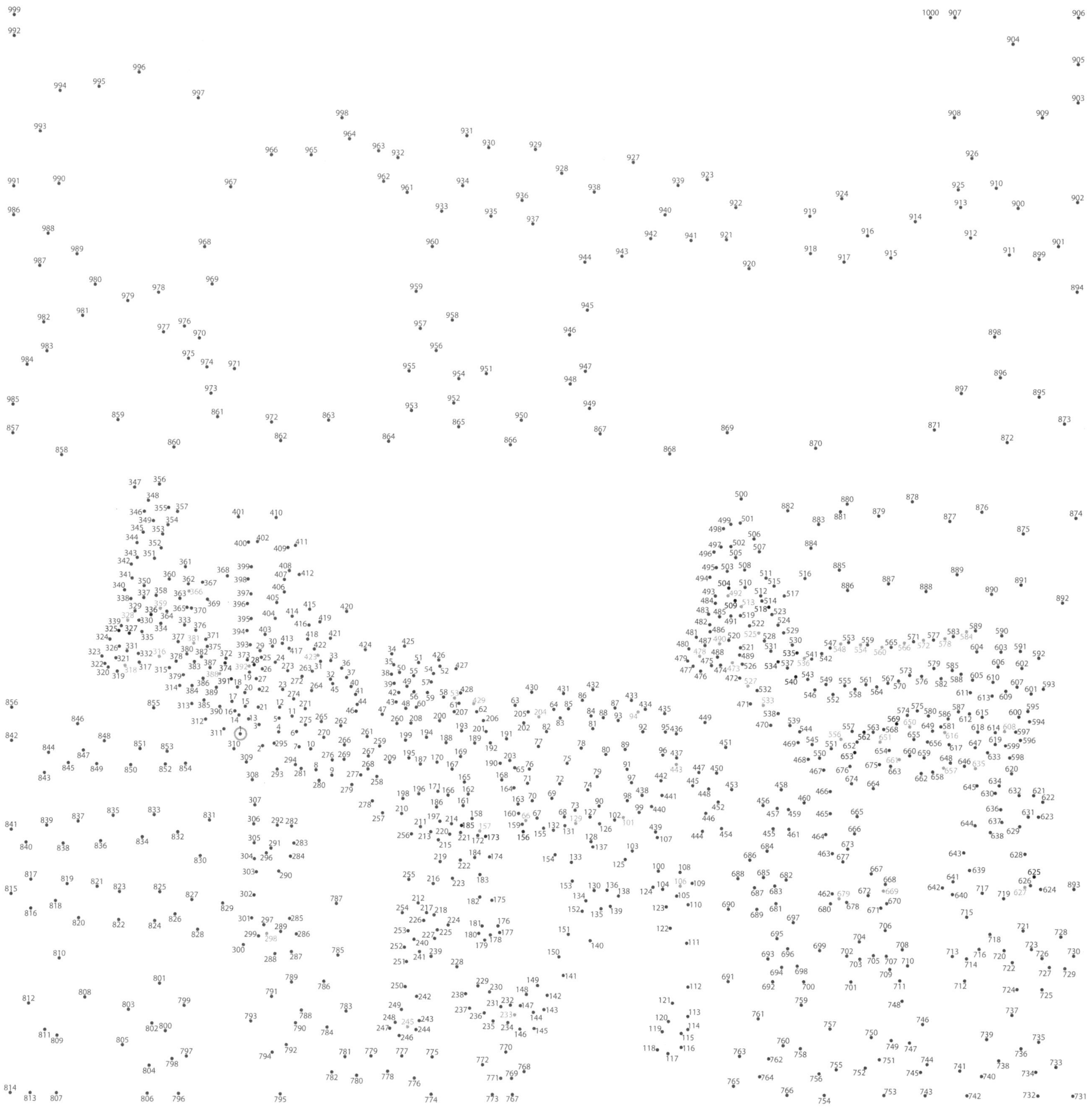

19. Crocodiles

Crocodiles are intelligent predators. They observe behavior, and will take advantage of routines, such as animals coming to drink at the same time each day. During the spring months, when birds are looking for material to build their nest, a crocodile will hide in shallow water, with twigs and sticks balanced on their snout. When an unsuspecting bird approaches to gather the sticks, the crocodile pounces.

20. Flamingoes

Flamingoes are social birds, and zoos have learned that populations of less than 15 will fail to thrive. One advantage of large colonies is that nesting sites are used more efficiently. Breeding groups will contain up to 50 birds, and both males and females perform ritual displays. This encourages birds to nest at the same time, which means that the chicks can gather together after hatching in "microcrèches."

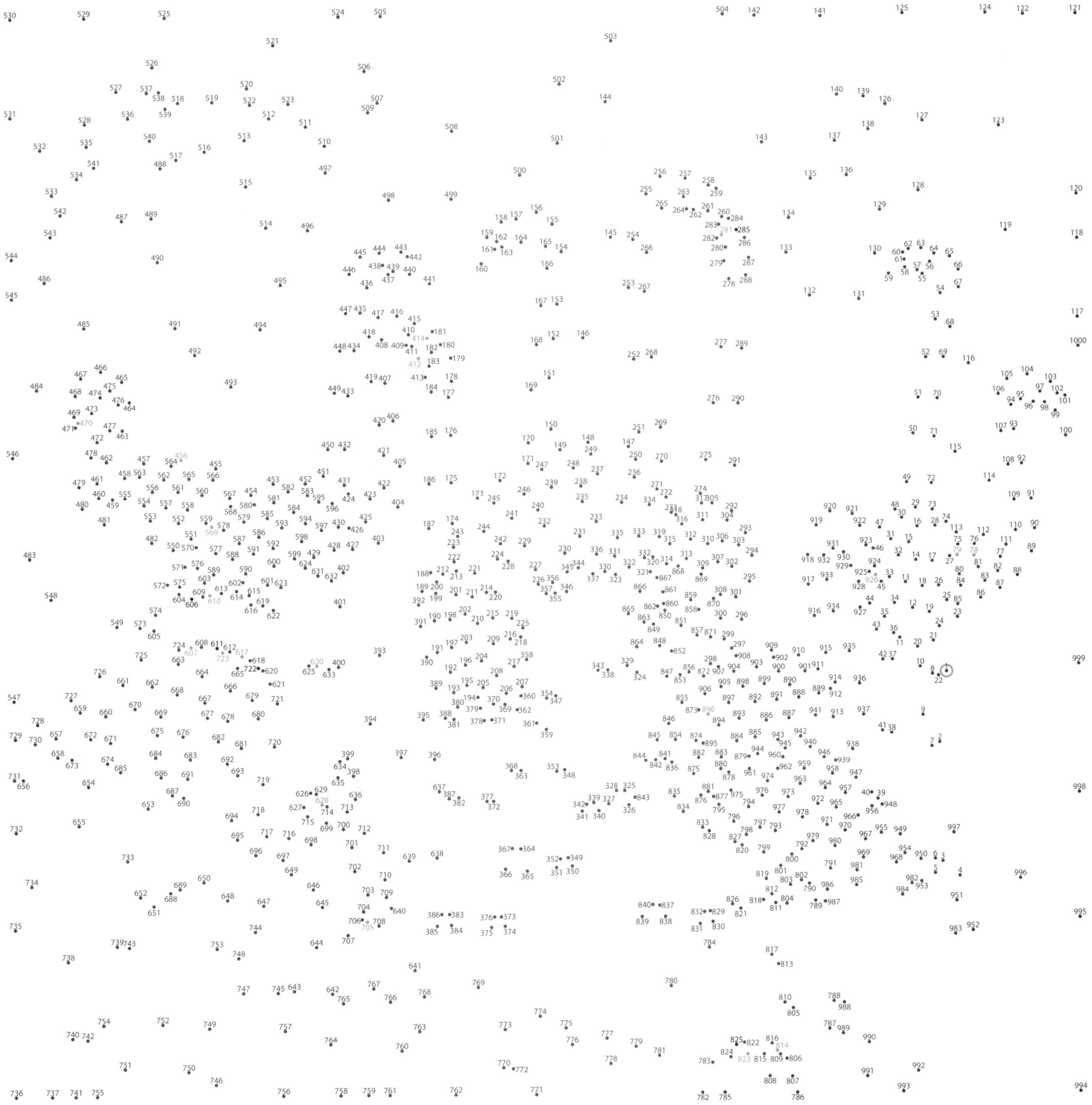

21. Tiger

Fossil remains found in China suggest that tigers date back to at least two million years ago. There were eight subspecies in the middle of the last century; today there are only five. This is the result of human activity; tigers have no natural predators. Tigers are one of the few cats to have stripes. It is assumed the light and shade offers good camouflage in jungle vegetation and long grass.

22. Penguins

Some species gather together in the thousands, so each penguin has a distinctive call for identification. Hunting in the water, they dive no deeper than 60 feet (18.3 meters) in search of their prey. Pursuing krill, fish, or squid in their beaks, they swallow their catch whole. This means they swallow saltwater, and a nasal gland located just above their eyes filters the salt from their bloodstream.

23. Alligator

The alligator is known for its fearsome bite, with a jaw that has evolved to close with a powerful bite. Curiously, however, the muscles that open the jaw are weak. An adult human can easily hold its jaws closed, and a few layers of duct tape will do the same. There are two species of alligator: the American and the Chinese. Of the latter, perhaps a few dozen remain in the wild.

24. Doris Longwing Butterflies

The Doris Longwing is found in Central America, from Mexico to the Amazon Basin, at sea level to an altitude of 3,940 feet (1,200 meters). Its colors and patterns vary considerably. The background is always black, with hite on the forewings, but it is punctuated by splashes of red, orange, blue, green, or silver. Such vivid coloration offers due warning that they are poisonous, which may explain why they have relatively few predators.

25. Yellow-Footed Tortoise

Also known as the Brazilian Giant Tortoise, this reptile is found in the Amazon Basin and is the largest tortoise on the mainland of South America. It is an omnivore, feeding not just on leaves, roots, and flowers, but also corpses, from deer to snakes. It swallows pebbles and sand, too, presumably to help with digestion. The tortoise is often seen close to water, and it is thought to favor humid conditions.

26. Rainbow Boa

This species of boa ranges from deep red to orange, with patterns on the side that look like a crescent moon. Its name, however, echoes a curious effect of their skin, which sometimes shines with all the colors of the rainbow. This is particularly true in sunlight, when tiny ridges on their skin act like prisms to refract the light. (Gasoline floating on water produces a similar effect.)

27. Toucan

The toucan's colorful beak may be up to one-third of the bird's size. Although this may seem awkward, it offers many advantages. It enables the toucan to reach deep into holes that others birds cannot access. It may intimidate smaller birds, whose nests they ransack. And it enables toucans to control their temperature; to cool down, they simply allow more blood to flow to their beak.

28. Starling

Starlings are native to Europe, Asia, Africa, and northern Australia and have been introduced to North America. These highly sociable birds may be found in flocks that include other species of birds. Fruits dominate their diets, and the birds are an important disperser of seeds. Many starlings also feed on nectar, which implies they have a role in pollination, too, although the extent of this is not clear.

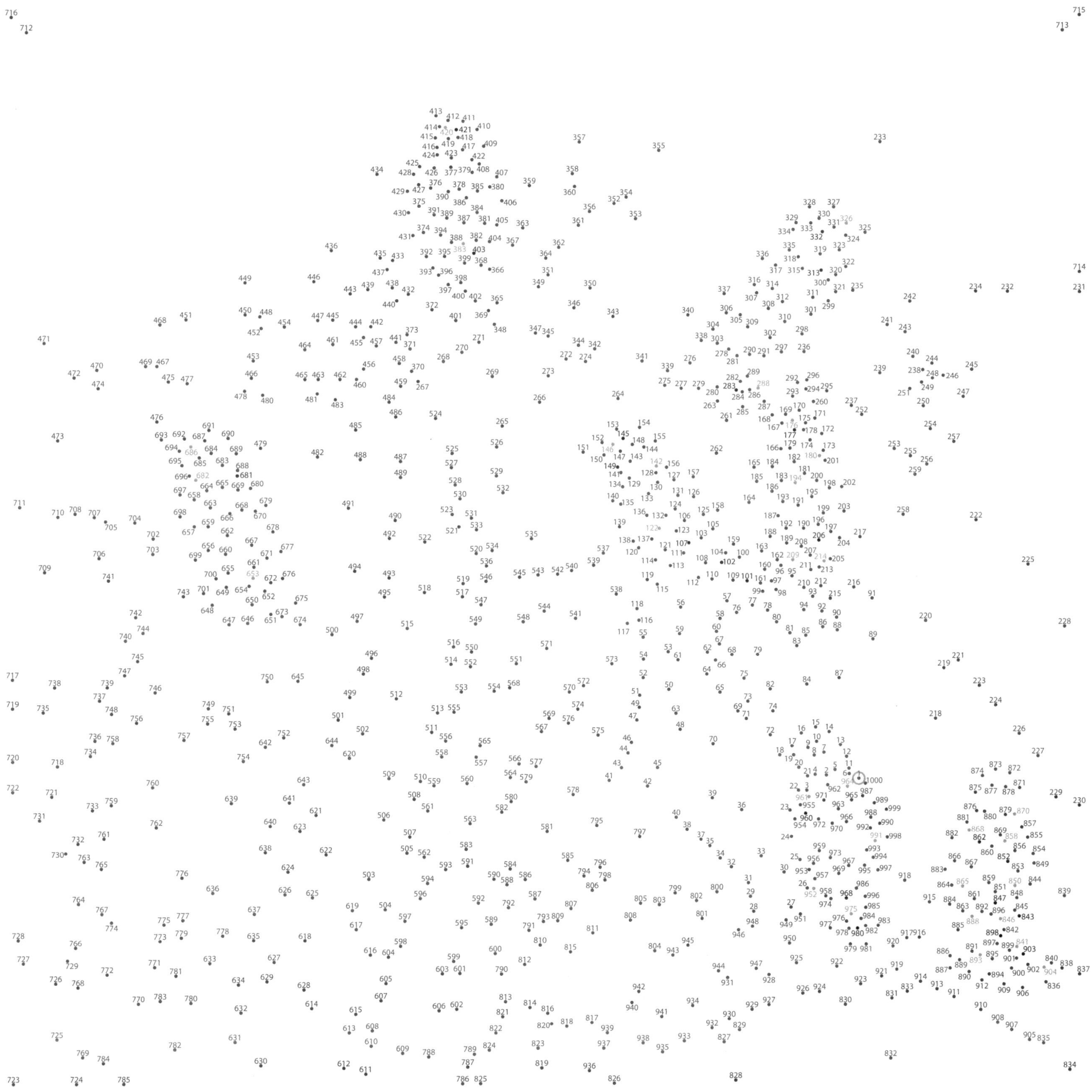

29. Warthog

Found on the open plains and grasslands of sub-Saharan Africa, warthogs can survive for months at a time without water. Like camels, they are able to tolerate high body temperatures, which helps them to conserve moisture that would otherwise be used for cooling. They drink regularly when water is available and like to submerge themselves in it to cool down. For the same reason, they also wallow in mud.

30. Antelope

Antelopes are intelligent animals, and some species follow the rains to find the grass that makes up most of their diet. In Africa, they often follow zebra, which eat the tougher grasses. Antelopes play an important role in the African food chain, offering a stable food source for a range of predators, from lions to crocodiles. In the wild, therefore, they rarely live more than ten years.

31. Hummingbird

Throughout the Americas are 320 species of hummingbird. Some are so small that they may be caught by a dragonfly or trapped in a spider web. They beat their wings between 12 and 90 times a second, and the humming that gives them their name varies between species accordingly. They can reach speeds of 34 miles per hour (54 kilometers per hour) and are also the only bird able to fly backward.

32. Jaguar

The jaguar is the largest cat in the Americas. An opportunist that will eat what it can catch, the jaguar preys on more than 80 species. It ambushes rather than chases its prey, attacking from cover and even leaping into the water. The jaguar sometimes uses a method of killing unique among the cat family. It bites the prey between the ears with its canine teeth, piercing the brain.

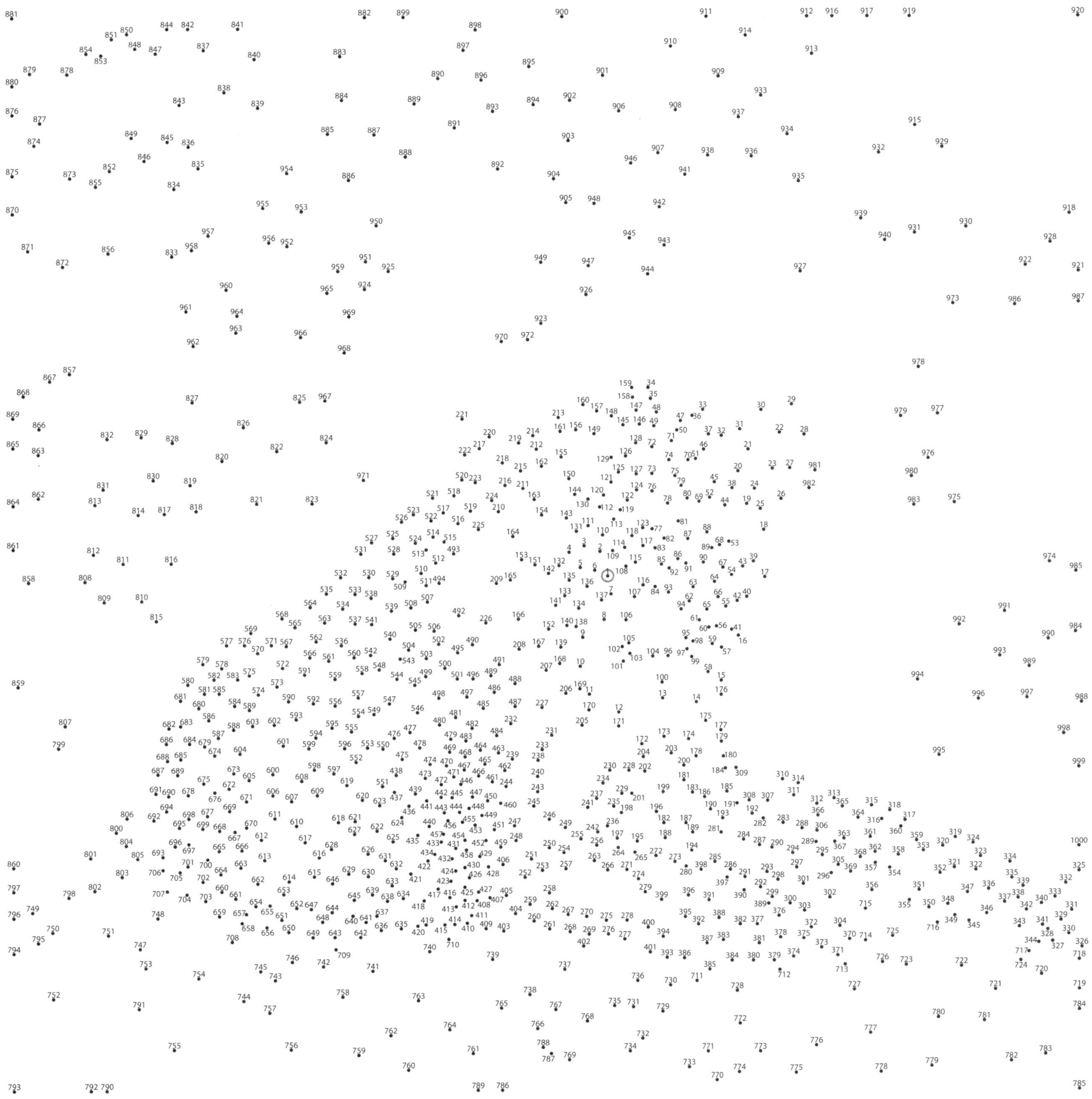

33. Monarch Butterfly

The orange, black, and white coloring of the monarch butterfly may be beautiful, but it serves as a warning. The milkweed nectar on which it almost exclusively feeds ensures that the butterfly is toxic. Monarchs may produce four generations in one summer. The first three generations continue the migration north, while the fourth survives for up to nine months and will begin the migration south.

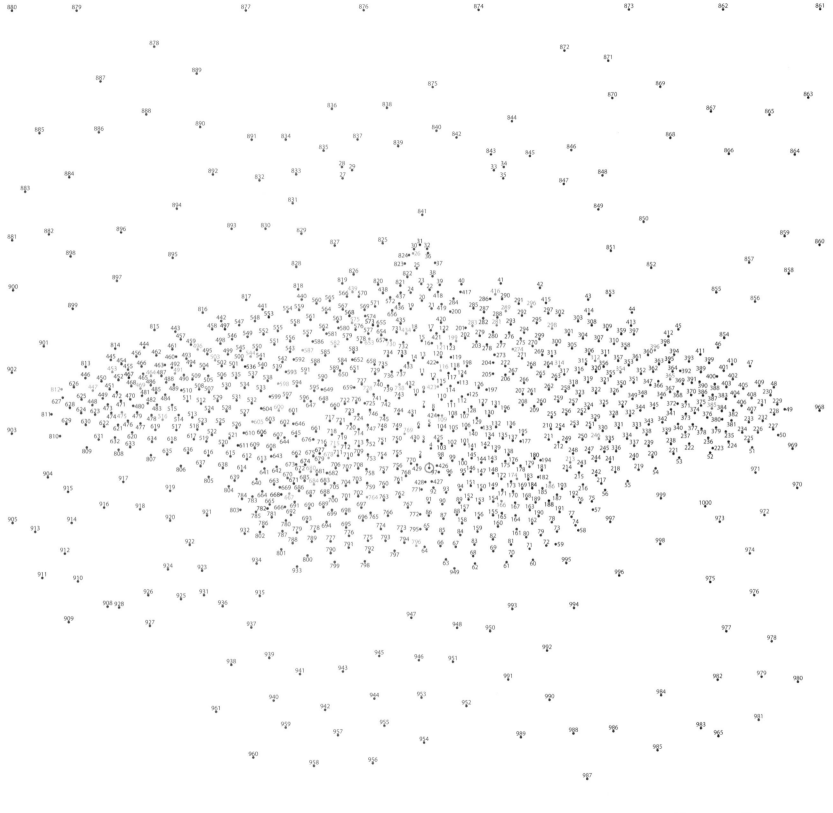

34. Scarlet Ibis

The red plumage of the Scarlet Ibis explains its name, and it is unique—no other shorebird has red feathers. The color comes from the shrimp and red shellfish it catches in its sensitive bill by probing in soft mud. However, these are by no means all it eats. Beetles and scarabs are an important part of its diet, too, and again its long curved beak proves useful, probing under leaves.

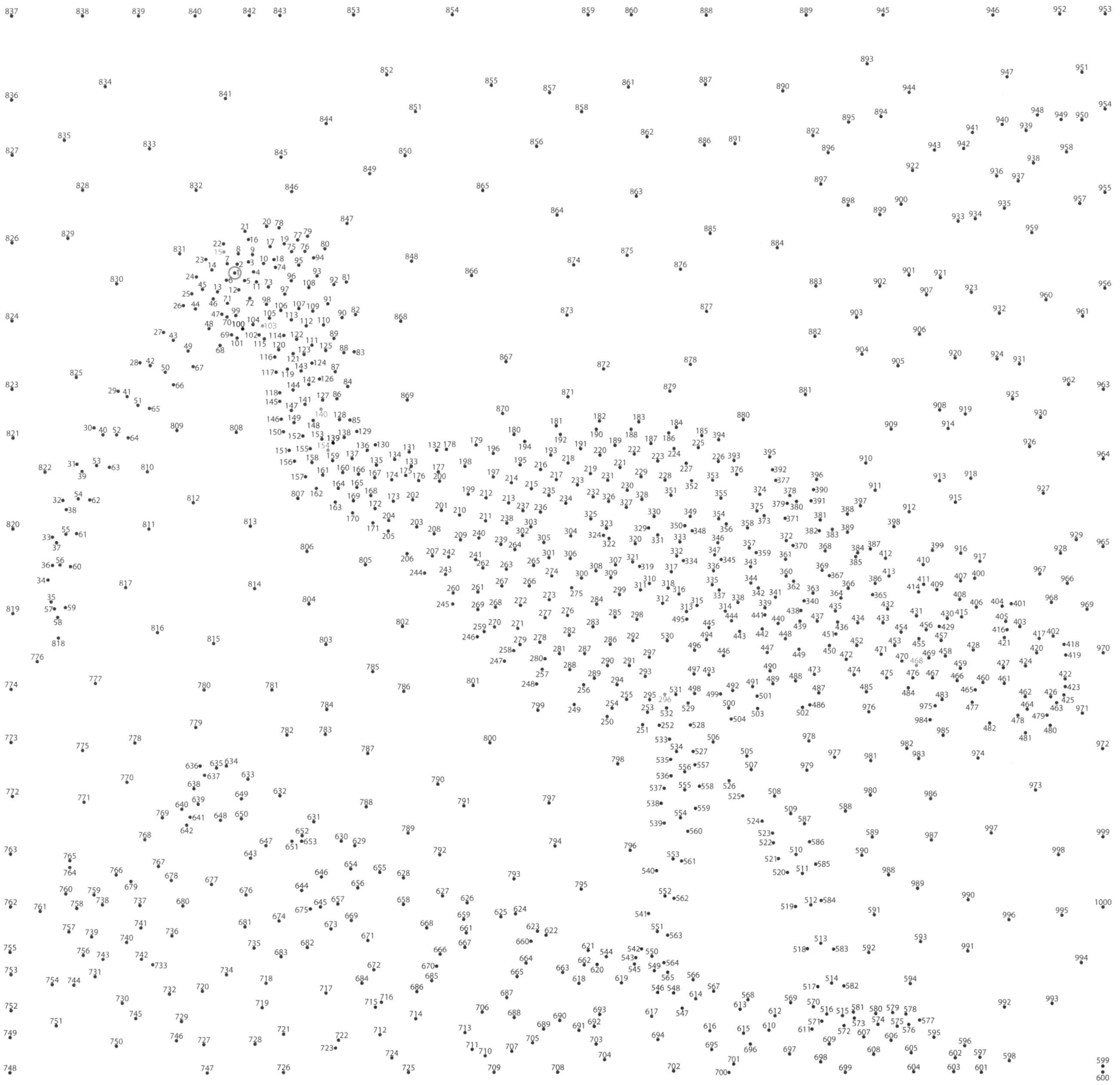

35. Leopard

The leopard has the largest distribution of any cat, found not just in Africa but also across Asia. It is found in a range of habitats, from forests to mountains, grasslands to deserts. The strongest member of the cat family and a skilled climber, the leopard often carries its prey into the trees to protect it from scavengers. It may leave it there for days, returning only when hungry.

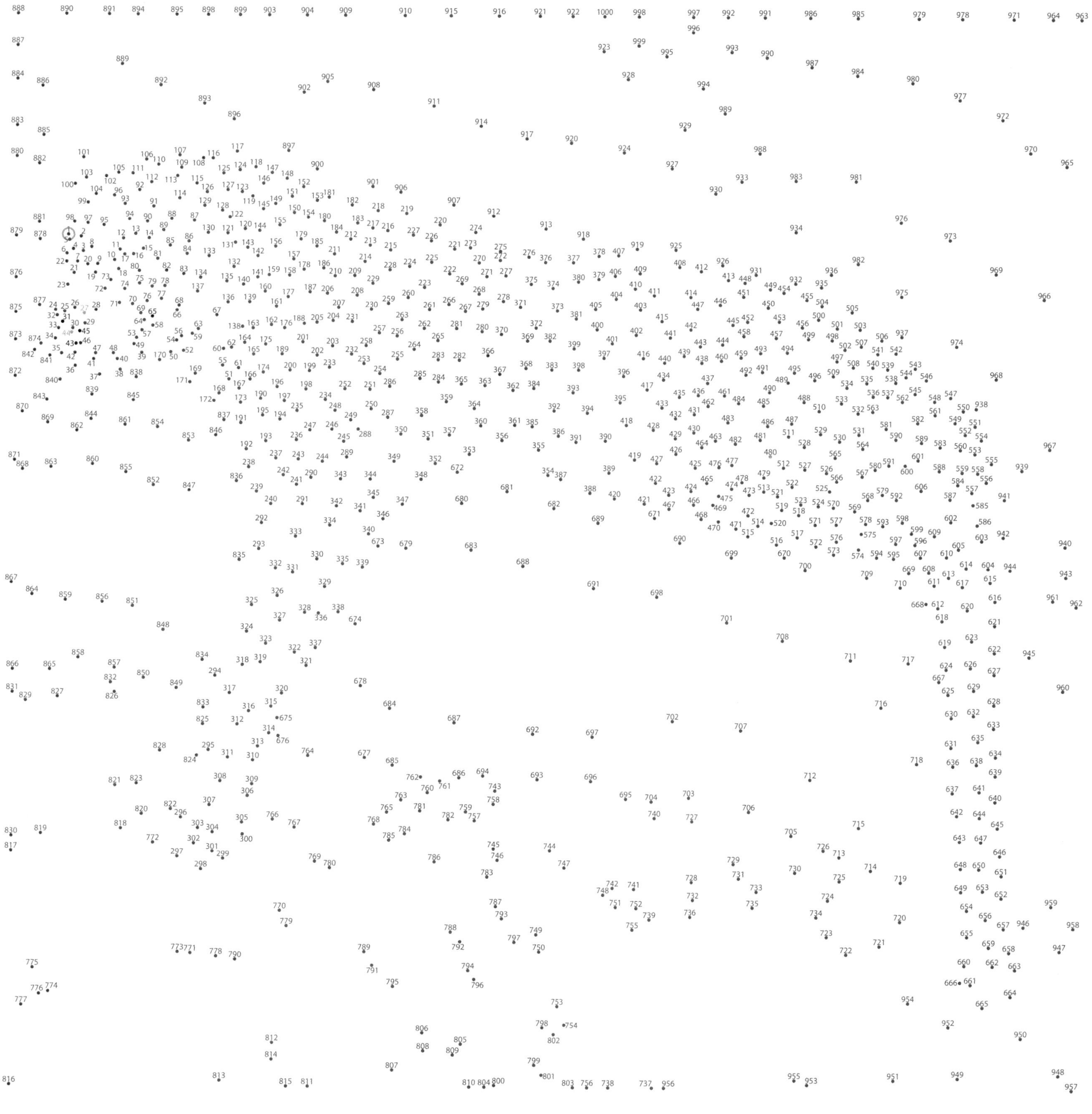

36. Brown Bear

The most widely distributed bear in the world, the brown bear is found across North America, Europe, and Asia. Their shoulder hump gives them a distinctive silhouette, thanks to powerful muscles that enable them to tear through logs, move rocks, and dig through heavy soil. Brown bears are omnivores and will consider eating whatever they find, and their diet varies with the seasons and their environment.

37. Orangutan

"Orangutan" means "person of the forest," and these highly intelligent primates are found only in the rainforests of Borneo and Sumatra. They spend most of their time in trees, and it seems that several plant species rely solely on orangutans to disperse their seeds. Unfortunately, deforestation means that orangutans are now endangered. In the last century, their total population has declined by 75 percent.

38. Squirrel Monkeys

The yellowish orange fur on its back explains why this New World primate is called the "squirrel monkey." Its name in Germanic languages may be even more apt: with a white throat and ears and a black mouth, it has earned the name "death's head monkey." It lives in the tropical rainforests of Central and South America and is highly adaptable; it is found in wetlands and mangrove forests, too.

39. Yellow-Billed Hornbill

The yellow-billed hornbill is found most often on the dry, open savannas of sub-Saharan Africa. They do favor woodlands, if they can find them—in particular, broad-leaved and acacia woodlands. In African folklore, the yellow-billed hornbill is a symbol of marital fidelity, which reflects its unusual nesting behavior. The female seals herself inside the nest, leaving an opening for the male to bring food. It's a strategy that offers good protection against predators.

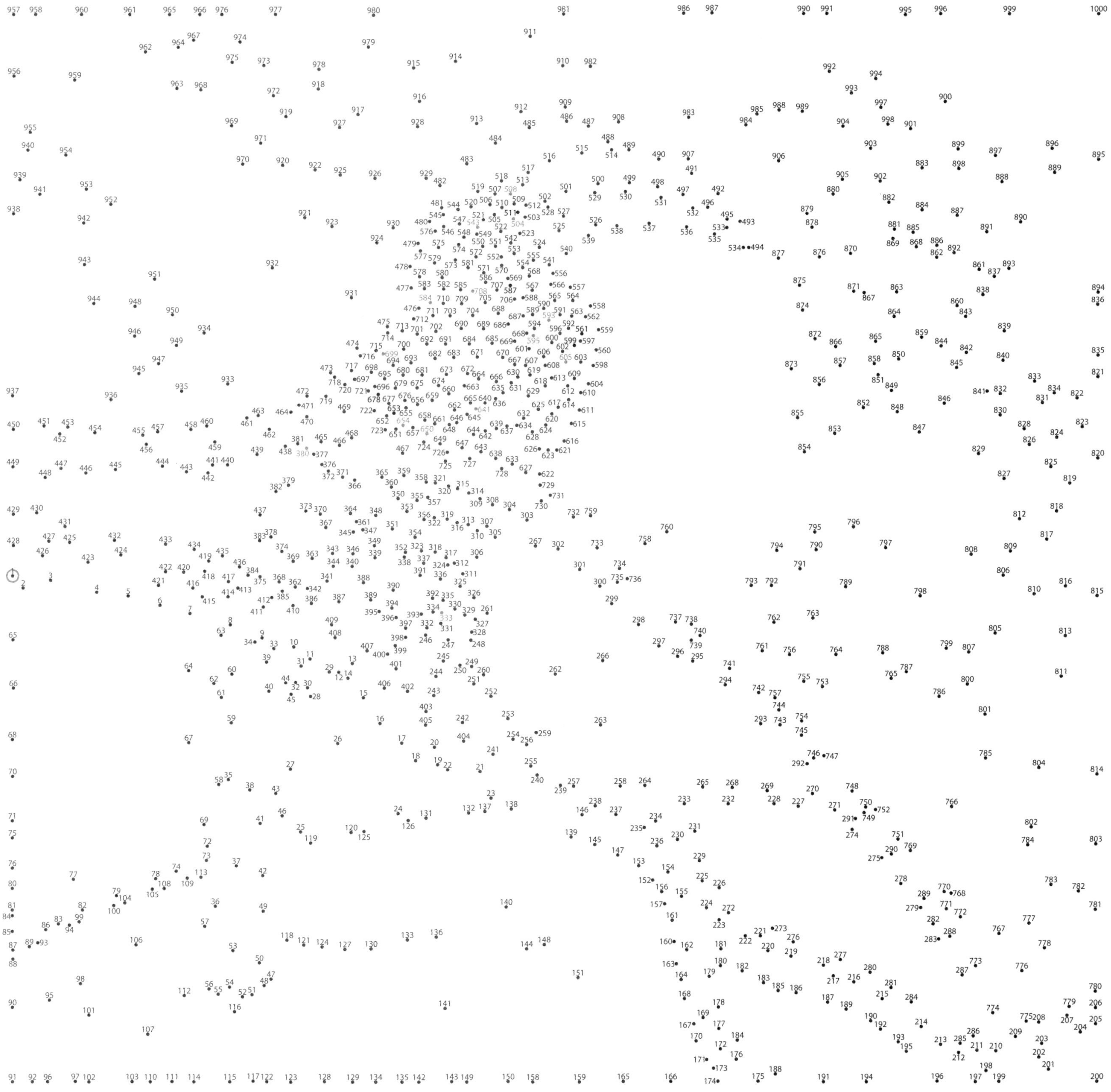

40. Sloth

On the ground, the sloth moves at about 6½ feet (2 meters) per minute. In the trees, the average is 10 feet (3 meters) per minute. This speed is so slow that a female may not mate in some years, simply because she fails to find a male. Curiously, however, such slow movement offers a form of protection. Green algae grow on their thick fur, providing camouflage that confuses predators.

41. Andean Cock-of-the-Rock

With its brilliant orange feathers, the Andean cock-of-the-rock is probably the most recognizable bird in the cloud forests of the Andes Mountains. The male also has a distinctive fan-shape crest. The bird's name refers to their preference for building nests on rocks and ledges. The female builds the nest alone, mixing her saliva with vegetable matter and mud, and shaping it into a cup. Abandoned nests may be renovated for use by other birds.

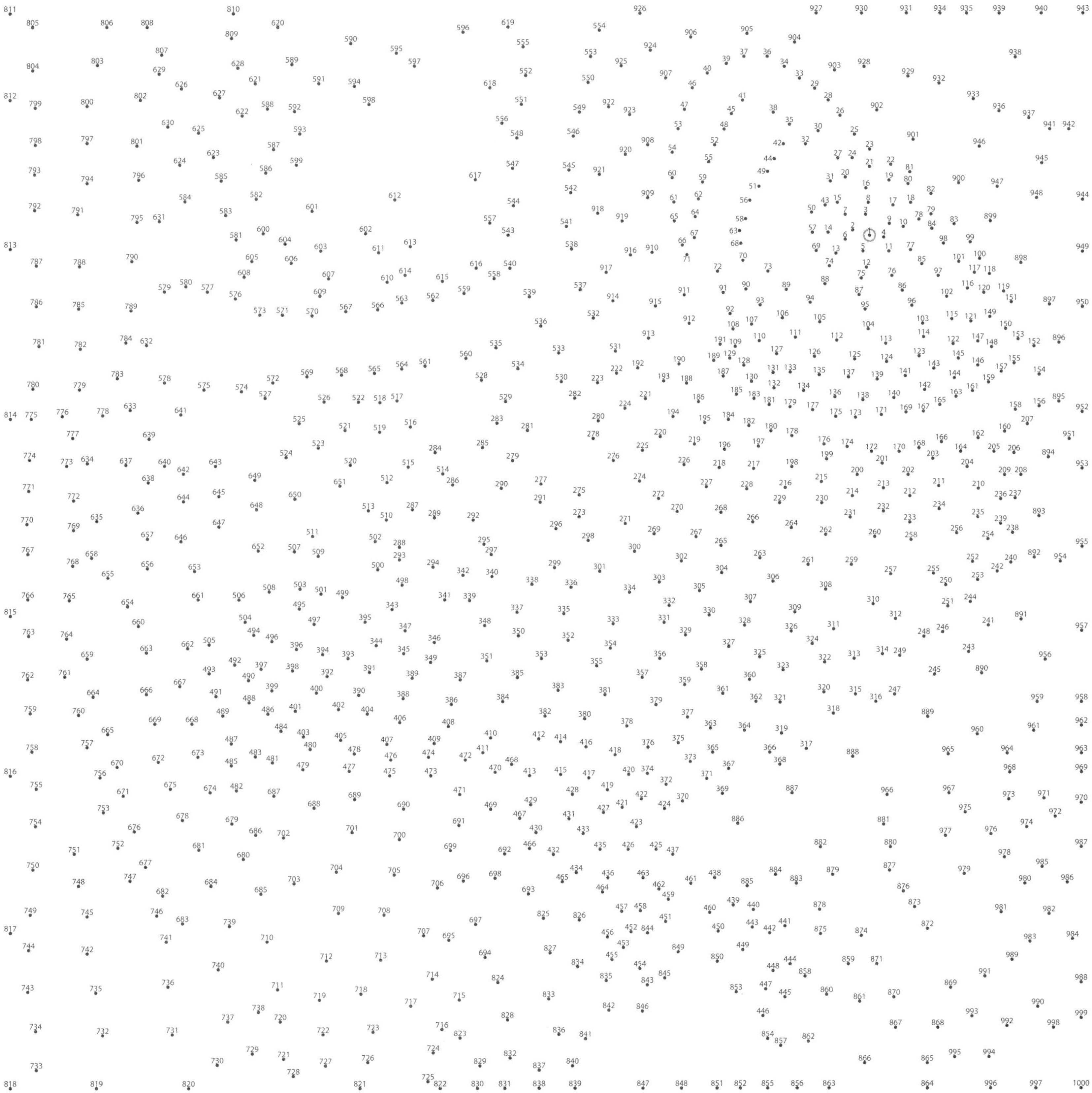

42. Meerkats

Meerkats are social animals that live in the grassland and deserts of southern Africa. About 20, but up to 50, individuals live together in a group known as a "mob," "gang," or "clan." Using their long, curved claws, they dig up to five different burrows on their territory, where they sleep at night. The clan forages together for food, but it will always have one sentry standing tall to watch out for predators.

1. Parrots

2. Giraffe

3. Gorilla

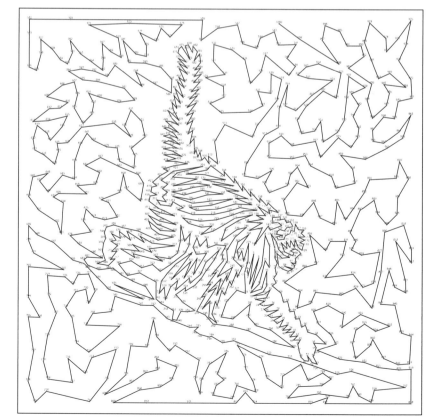

4. Spider Monkey

5. Elephant

6. Chimpanzee

7. Panda

8. Red-Eye Frog

9. Lizard

10. Spotted Hyena

11. Chameleon

12. Zebra

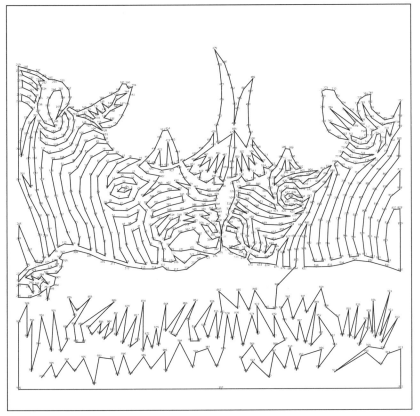

13. Rhinoceros

14. Lions

15. Vulture

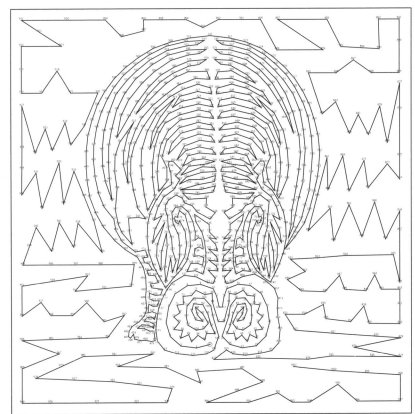

16. Hippopotamus

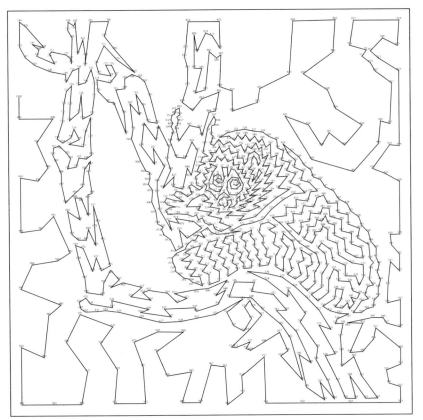

17. Slow Loris

18. Gazelles

19. Crocodiles

20. Flamingoes

21. Tiger

22. Penguins

23. Alligator

24. Doris Longwing Butterflies

25. Yellow-Footed Tortoise

26. Rainbow Boa

27. Toucan

28. Starling

29. Warthog

30. Antelope

31. Hummingbird

32. Jaguar

33. Monarch Butterfly

34. Scarlet Ibis

35. Leopard

36. Brown Bear